SHARK ATTACK !

W9-DHK-959

THIS BOOK BELONGS TO:

....

....

WHAT IS A SHARK?

Sharks are large fish that live in oceans and hunt other animals. They have amazing bodies, super senses, and great killing skills.

SENSES

Sharks can hear, see, and smell their prey. They also have a special electric sense that tells them when another animal is nearby.

GILLS

Big land animals breathe using lungs. Fish breathe using gills.

MASSIVE JAWS

Sharks have huge, gaping mouths containing lots of very sharp teeth.

Blue shark

BENDY BODIES

Shark skeletons are not made of bone. They are made of a bendy, rubbery substance called cartilage.

BODY SHAPE

Most sharks have long, slender bodies that are perfect for swimming at speed. This body shape is called streamlined.

SHARK FACT

A SHARK'S SKIN IS COVERED IN TINY TOOTHLIKE PLATES. THEY ARE SHAPED TO HELP WATER GLIDE OVER THEM SMOOTHLY.

YES OR NO?

Use your mini-stickers to choose the right answer.

1. Are sharks fish?

2. Do sharks live in forests?

3. Do sharks use gills to breathe?

TYPES OF SHARK

There are about **400** different types of shark. Many of them are huge, fierce hunters, while others are smaller and much more timid.

Great white shark

Speedy hunters

Body type:	Streamlined
Hunts:	Fast-swimming fish, dolphins, and seals
Examples:	Great white, shortfin mako

FEAR FACTOR

Shy sharks

Body type:	Small to medium, often patterned
Hunts:	Fish, squid, or animals on the seabed
Examples:	Horn sharks, collared carpet sharks

FEAR FACTOR

Slow and steady

Body type:	Extra large
Hunts:	Tiny animals called plankton
Examples:	Basking shark, whale shark

FEAR FACTOR

SHARK FACT

SHARKS HAVE BEEN AROUND FOR ABOUT 350 MILLION YEARS—THAT MAKES THEM OLDER THAN DINOSAURS!

Freaky and fierce

Body type:	Strange heads or snouts
Hunts:	Fish, squid, or animals on the seabed
Examples:	Sawsharks, hammerheads

FEAR FACTOR

Hammerhead shark

Can-you-see-me sharks

Body type:	Flattened and often patterned
Hunts:	Crabs, fish, and other animals near the seabed
Examples:	Angelsharks, wobbegongs

FEAR FACTOR

Tiger shark

Coastal cruisers

Body type:	Streamlined
Hunts:	Fish, squid, seals, dolphins
Examples:	Tiger shark, lemon shark

FEAR FACTOR

LITTLE AND LARGE

Whale sharks are the largest fish in the world, but they are harmless to humans. The smallest sharks are shorter than your arm.

Whale shark

GENTLE GIANTS

Whale sharks are about 40 feet (12.2m) long. They swim with their wide mouths open so they can suck in and swallow water and small animals.

LARGEST FISH

WHICH SHARK?

?

Read the text and choose the correct stickers.

This shark can crunch shells.

Spined pygmy sharks are less than 10 inches (25cm) long. They spend the day hiding in deep water and swim to the surface at night to feed.

MEDIUM-SIZED

Port Jackson sharks grow to about 40 inches (1m) long. They have big, crushing teeth that crunch through starfish, shells, and sea urchins.

Port Jackson

This is the world's biggest fish.

SHARK FACT

A WHALE SHARK IS TEN TIMES BIGGER THAN A PORT JACKSON SHARK.

A WORLD OF SHARKS

Our planet holds 333 million cubic miles (1.36 billion km³) of water in five oceans—the Pacific, Atlantic, Arctic, Indian, and the Southern.

Greenland shark

Greenland sharks live in icy oceans near the North Pole. They are huge sharks that swim slowly.

Blue shark

Blue sharks are great swimmers. A female can swim up to 1,200 miles (2000km) in just four months.

8

TRUE OR FALSE?

Use your mini-stickers to choose the right answer.

√ X

1 Greenland sharks live in hot oceans.

Oceanic whitetip

Oceanic whitetips spend their lives in the open ocean, looking for fish, stingrays, and turtles to eat.

Epaulette shark

The epaulette shark makes its home in the shallow, tropical waters surrounding Australia and New Guinea.

Lemon shark

Lemon sharks are common near coasts with warmer waters. Small suckerfish often hitch a ride on them.

SHARK FACT

MOST SHARKS STAY CLOSE TO THE COAST, WHERE THE WATER IS SHALLOW AND THERE IS PLENTY OF FOOD TO BE FOUND.

✓ ✗ ?   ✓ ✗ ?

2 Blue sharks can swim far.

3 Sharks do not like to live near the coast.

MEET THE FAMILY

Skates and rays are members of the shark family. Like sharks, skates and rays live in oceans and their skeletons are made of bendy cartilage.

Manta ray

MASSIVE MANTAS

Manta rays are huge fish that grow to 30 feet (9.1m) wide. They swim slowly, flapping their giant "wings," and eat small sea organisms called plankton.

SHARK FACT

A MANTA RAY'S DAILY DIET WEIGHS AS MUCH AS 240 BURGERS.

SMALL SKATES

Skates live in deep water and are usually smaller than rays. The winter skate is about 40 inches (1.2m) long, with spines on its back and tail.

Stingray

Stingrays have flat bodies and long tails. At the end of the tail is a sharp spine that delivers a nasty dose of venom.

Manta rays are also called "devilfish", but they are harmless to humans.

?

Rays have patterns and colors on their skin. This helps them to hide on the seabed.

RAY OR SKATE?

Winter skate

It is hard to find this flat-bodied fish on the seabed.

This fish lives in deep water.

MONSTER CHOPPERS

Sharks are famous for their large, gleaming, sharp teeth, which they use to catch and kill slippery or strong animals.

Shortfi mako

A shortfin mako has long, sharp, spearlike teeth.

GREAT WHITE SHARK

A great white shark has hundreds of teeth, which are arranged in rows.

TRUE OR FALSE?

Use your mini-stickers to choose the right answer.

1 All sharks have just 20 teeth, like childrer

Frilled sharks' teeth are arranged into 25 sets. Each set of teeth has five teeth with three cusps.

-rilled shark

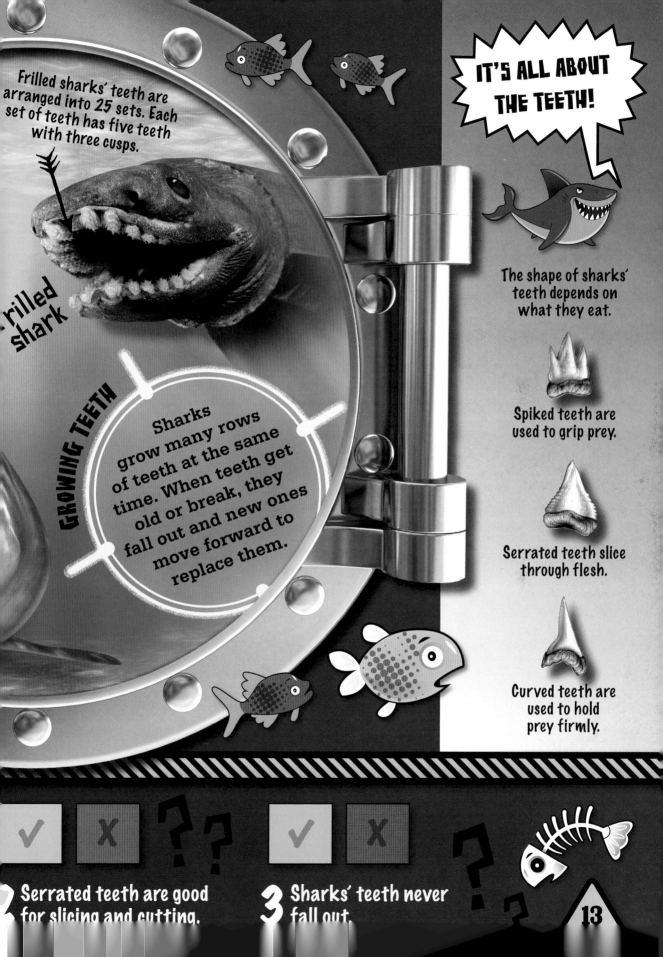

GROWING TEETH

Sharks grow many rows of teeth at the same time. When teeth get old or break, they fall out and new ones move forward to replace them.

IT'S ALL ABOUT THE TEETH!

The shape of sharks' teeth depends on what they eat.

Spiked teeth are used to grip prey.

Serrated teeth slice through flesh.

Curved teeth are used to hold prey firmly.

2 Serrated teeth are good for slicing and cutting.

3 Sharks' teeth never fall out.

TAILS AND FINS

A shark's tail is packed with powerful swimming muscles. Fins also help a shark to swim in the right direction, and they stop it from rolling over.

Angelshark

ANGEL WINGS

The pectoral fins of flat-bodied sharks, such as angelsharks, are often very long, winglike fins. They help the sharks to hide on the seabed.

dorsal fin

tail

anal fin

pelvic fin

WHICH SHARK?

Read the text and choose the correct stickers.

This shark likes to whack its prey with its tail.

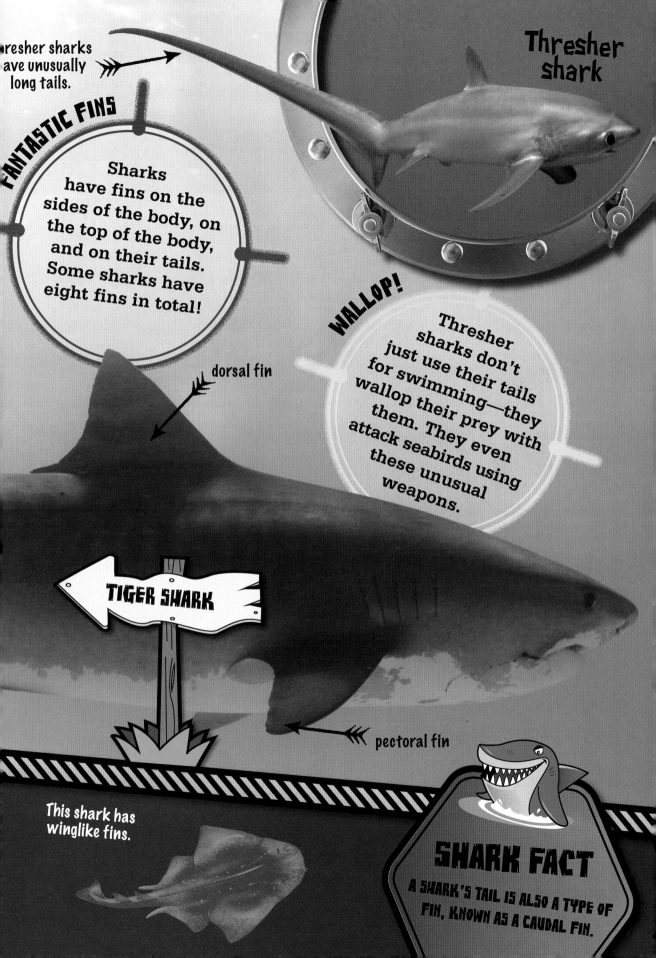

resher sharks
ave unusually
long tails.

Thresher shark

FANTASTIC FINS

Sharks have fins on the sides of the body, on the top of the body, and on their tails. Some sharks have eight fins in total!

dorsal fin

WALLOP!

Thresher sharks don't just use their tails for swimming—they wallop their prey with them. They even attack seabirds using these unusual weapons.

TIGER SHARK

pectoral fin

This shark has winglike fins.

SHARK FACT

A SHARK'S TAIL IS ALSO A TYPE OF FIN, KNOWN AS A CAUDAL FIN.

COLORS AND CAMOUFLAGE

Sharks that swim near the seabed have skin that is patterned or colored to help them hide. This is called camouflage.

SPOTS

Leopard sharks and whale sharks have spotted skin. It helps them to hide from their unsuspecting prey in shallow water, where sunlight creates shadows.

The dark marks on a leopard shark's back fade as it gets older.

SPOT THE DIFFERENCE

These two whale sharks look similar. How many differences can you count? Use a mini-sticker to mark the right answer.

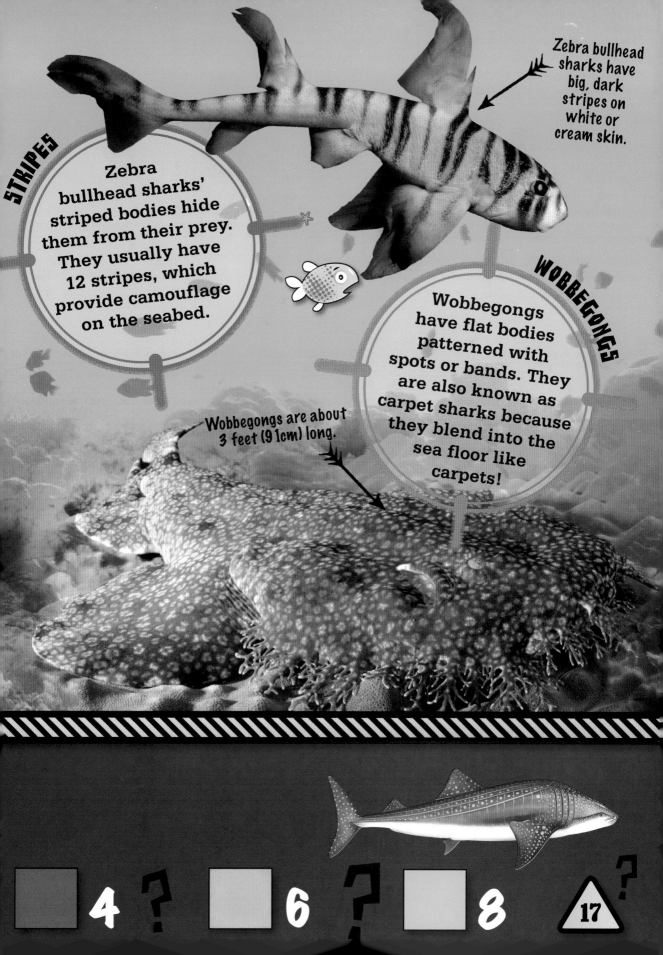

STRIPES

Zebra bullhead sharks have big, dark stripes on white or cream skin.

Zebra bullhead sharks' striped bodies hide them from their prey. They usually have 12 stripes, which provide camouflage on the seabed.

WOBBEGONGS

Wobbegongs have flat bodies patterned with spots or bands. They are also known as carpet sharks because they blend into the sea floor like carpets!

Wobbegongs are about 3 feet (91cm) long.

HUGE HAMMERHEADS

There are ten types of hammerhead shark and they all share one thing—huge, wide heads with eyes at the tips.

BIG AND BOLD

Most hammerheads are large and like to hunt fish. They swim near the shore, often gathering in groups to feed on shoals of fish.

Scalloped hammerhead

Bonnethead sharks are one of the smallest types of hammerhead and are usually just 40 inches (1.2m) long.

Bonnethead

SHARK FACT

GREAT HAMMERHEADS CAN GROW TO MORE THAN 20 FEET (6M) LONG!

Scientists think that the hammerheads' head shape helps them to change direction quickly and to find their prey.

Hammerheads have small mouths compared to the size of their heads.

Great hammerhead

SCRAMBLED SHARKS

These shark names have gotten scrambled. Do you know what they should say? Put a sticker next to the ones you know.

1 E H A M D M A H R M E R

2 O M A N K I F H S O R T N

3 K T R O C P A J N O S S

19

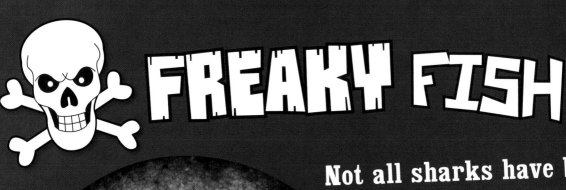

FREAKY FISH

Not all sharks have big, streamlined bodies. In fact, some of them look downright odd. Although these sharks may be a bit freaky, they are fascinating, too.

PORT JACKSON SHARK

Port Jackson sharks are often compared to pigs because they have broad heads with big nostrils and rows of tiny teeth.

QUICK QUIZ

Use your mini-stickers to mark the right answer.

1 What does a Port Jackson shark look like?

A goblin

A pig

Lanternshark

GLOW-IN-THE-DARK

Lanternsharks live in deep oceans where sunshine cannot reach, and they glow in the dark to tempt tasty fish to swim close by.

SCARED STIFF

When a swell shark is scared it swallows water until its body swells to twice its normal size in order to frighten attackers away.

Swell shark

FREAK SHOW!

2 Which shark is the smallest?

A swell shark

A dwarf lanternshark

3 Why is it dark in the deep ocean?

Sunlight can't reach there.

Water turns black when it is deep.

SHARK QUIZ

TIC TAC TOE

Use your mini-stickers to play this classic game.

Greenland shark

This huge, slow shark lives in cold places.

WHICH FISH?

Use your finger to trace the lines, and discover which unlucky fish was caught by the shark.

HUNGRY STAN

Stan the stingray eats two fish a day for five days. How many fish does he eat altogether?

7 □ **5** □ **10** □

This ray can grow to 30 feet (9m) wide.

Manta ray

SHARK FACT

EPAULETTE SHARKS USE THEIR FINS LIKE LEGS TO WALK ON THE SEABED!

WORD-WISE

Sharks are predators. What is a predator?

 An animal that eats fish.

 An animal that hunts other animals to eat.

WEIRD BUT TRUE

Put a mini-sticker next to the correct answer:

1 Which of the following is most deadly?

 Leopard

 Great white shark

 Indian cobra

2 A great white shark is about 15 times heavier than a human.

 ✓ True

 X False

3 Which shark has the biggest mouth?

□ Tiger shark

□ Great white shark

□ Basking shark

23

SPEEDY HUNTERS

Hungry sharks are very fast. As they swim, they bend their bodies from side to side and keep their eyes fixed on their prey.

Shortfin makos can leap up to 40 feet (12.2m) out of the water to catch their prey.

THE FASTEST SHARKS

Shortfin mako sharks are the fastest sharks. They live in warm water, because being warm helps their muscles to work faster.

Shortfin mako shark

SHARK FACT

SHORTFIN MAKOS CAN REACH TOP SPEEDS OF MORE THAN 30 MPH (48KPH).

20

WHICH SHARK?

Read the text and choose the correct stickers.

This is the fastest shark.

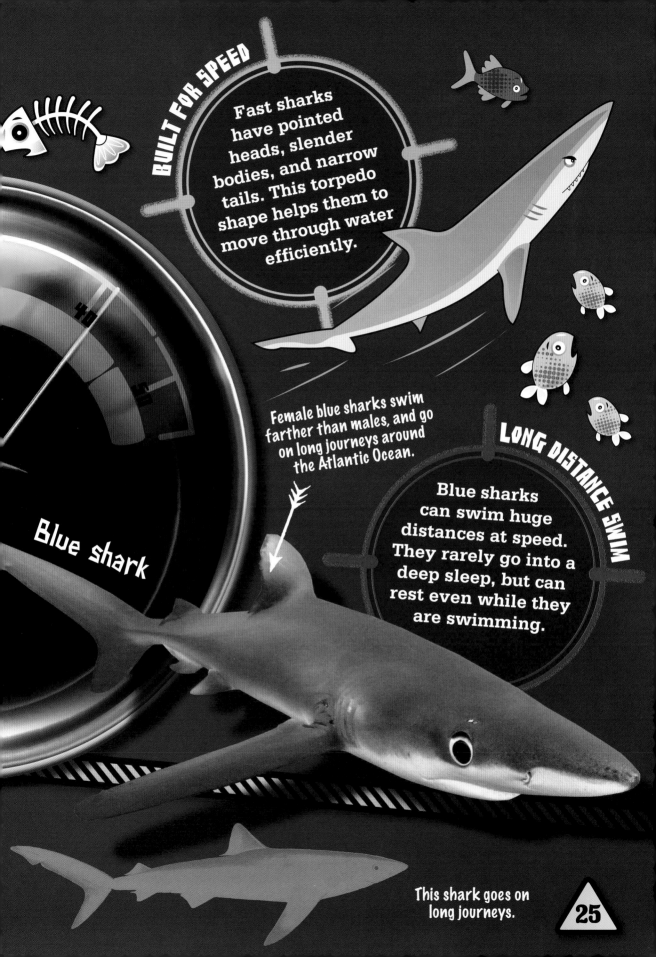

BUILT FOR SPEED

Fast sharks have pointed heads, slender bodies, and narrow tails. This torpedo shape helps them to move through water efficiently.

Female blue sharks swim farther than males, and go on long journeys around the Atlantic Ocean.

LONG DISTANCE SWIM

Blue sharks can swim huge distances at speed. They rarely go into a deep sleep, but can rest even while they are swimming.

Blue shark

This shark goes on long journeys.

25

WHAT DO SHARKS EAT?

All sharks eat other animals. Some sharks eat large mammals, such as seals. Others eat tiny sea creatures.

FISH FOOD

Sharks that live in the open ocean often hunt fish. They chase shoals of fish, and feed in a frenzy when they catch them.

SEABED SHARKS

Sharks that live on the seabed eat shelled animals that live there, such as crabs, as well as other fish.

Sardines are silvery fish that live in huge shoals. Fast sharks can grab a big mouthful of fish in a single attack.

Crabs have tough outer shells. Sharks that eat them need strong jaws and teeth that crunch, not slice.

Squid and octopuses are cousins of slugs and snails. Their bodies are soft and slippery.

Sandtiger shark

Sharks that live near the shore, such as sandtiger sharks, eat a mixture of foods, but squid is a favorite treat.

Seals are packed with meat and fat, which makes them a perfect meal for a great white.

HUGE APPETITES

Big sharks hunt down large animals. They have the power, speed, and enormous jaws needed to catch and crunch through a seal's body.

Great white shark

LIFE ON A CORAL REEF

Many sharks make their homes on coral reefs. The water is clean, clear, warm, and full of tasty things to eat.

CARIBBEAN REEF SHARK

SHARK FACT

A SINGLE CORAL POLYP CAN LIVE FOR HUNDREDS OF YEARS. A CORAL REEF MAY BE THOUSANDS OF YEARS OLD.

GOOD HEARING

Caribbean reef sharks swim in shallow water, and sometimes rest on the seabed. They wait there and use their acute hearing to sense prey.

During the day, nurse sharks hide in cracks and gaps in the reef. At night, they come out to feed on shellfish, crabs, and coral polyps.

Nurse shark

GROUP HUNTERS

Whitetip reef sharks often hunt in groups. They feed on fish, such as parrotfish and damselfish, as well as octopuses.

Whitetip reef shark

29

STILL HUNGRY?

Most sharks are happy eating fish and other sea creatures, but some have developed a taste for more unusual types of food...

SHARK SHOCKER!

Seabirds taking a rest on the ocean surface, or diving into the water for fish, should watch out. A hungry shark may be waiting for them...

TRASHCAN TIGERS

Tiger sharks are not fussy. They are happy to eat almost anything they find—and that includes car tires, chickens, plastic bottles, and metal cans.

Tiger shark

? WHICH SHARK?

Read the text and then choose the correct stickers.

Basking shark

Basking sharks have enormous mouths, measuring over 3 feet (91cm) wide, but they eat tiny sea creatures.

ROTTEN RATFISH

Ratfish are strange shark cousins that live on the seafloor. They enjoy a menu of worms and crabs and sometimes even eat their own eggs and babies!

Ratfish

This shark cousin eats worms.

This big-mouthed shark eats tiny animals

31

SENSITIVE SHARKS

Finding food in the ocean can be difficult. The water is deep and dark, and oceans are huge. Sharks have some great senses that help them hunt.

SHARK FACT

SHARKS CAN SENSE JUST ONE DROP OF BLOOD IN A BATHTUB OF WATER.

BULL SHARK

SMELLING GOOD

Sharks have noses and they are super-sensitive to smells, especially the smells of blood and urine!

EYE EYE

Like cats, sharks are able to see in dim light. Sharks' eyes are on the sides of their heads, which means they can see all around them.

Sharks have taste buds all over their mouths and throats. They may bite an animal, decide they don't like the taste, and spit it out!

A nurse shark can even use its barbels to feel an animal in the dark.

Nurse shark

TOUCHY-FEELY

Some sharks have sensitive barbels hanging off their snouts. They use these to feel for animals hiding on the seabed.

HEAR HEAR

Silky sharks have such good hearing that they can hear low sounds from at least a quarter of a mile (400m) away.

Use your mini-stickers to choose the right answer.

YES OR NO

1. Do sharks have noses?

YES OR NO

2. Can sharks only see what's right in front of them?

YES OR NO

3. Do sharks like blood?

33

ELECTRIC SENSE

All animals use electricity to make their muscles move. Sharks can sense electricity and this special sense makes them fearsome predators.

Sawsharks use their long snouts to sense the electricity made by animals hiding in mud. They then swipe their snout through the mud to uncover their prey.

Sawsharks have barbels on their saws, so they can feel prey as well as sensing them.

Sawshark

WHICH SHARK?

Read the text and choose the correct stickers.

?

Hammerhead shark

Hammerheads sense electrical pulses, then sweep their heads from side to side to get a better idea of exactly where the pulses are coming from.

The holes around the shark's head sense electricity and send messages to its brain.

SHOCKING SHOT

Electric rays turn electricity into a weapon. First, they fire a warning shot to an attacker, then deliver a deadly shock.

An electric ray can use its electric power to defend itself or to stun its prey.

Electric ray

This odd-headed shark is great at finding prey.

A shark with a super-sensitive snout.

IN FOR THE KILL

Once a shark has found its victim it is time to go in for the kill. The shark needs skill, speed, and deadly weapons to catch its victim.

I SMELL LUNCH!

Sandtiger shark

CRUNCH TIME

Sharks have strong, crushing jaws. Goblin sharks can even move their jaws forward, out of their mouths, so they can grab their prey more quickly.

Movable jaws

WHICH SHARK?

Read the text and choose the correct stickers.

SNEAKY SHARKS

Bull sharks are extremely deadly sharks. They live in murky water and use their super senses to sneak up on their prey without being seen.

Bull sharks will attack almost anything—fish, dolphins, and even other sharks.

Bull shark

Sharks can swim toward their prey in almost total silence.

TIME FOR SPEED

Speedy sandtiger sharks keep their eyes fixed on their prey, following its movements and smell, as it tries to escape. Soon, the chase is on!

This big shark sneaks up on its prey.

This shark chases its prey.

GREAT WHITE SHARKS

Large, powerful body

Great whites are the most feared sharks. These superb hunters have power, speed, and huge, biting teeth.

Massive mouth with rows of teeth

SPY HOPPING

Hungry great white sharks often pop their heads out of the water to look for prey, such as seals. This is called spy-hopping.

POOR PERCY!

? Percy the fish is being chased by two lemon sharks, four blue sharks, and six great whites. How many sharks are after him?

38

Some great whites leap out of the water to grab their prey.

SHARK SUPPER

Great whites feed on big, meaty animals such as seals and sharks. They also hunt other large fish, seabirds, and turtles.

SHARK FACT

GREAT WHITES HUNT IN SHALLOW WATER WHERE HUMANS MIGHT BE SWIMMING, DIVING, WASHING, OR FISHING. LUCKILY, THEY DON'T LIKE THE TASTE OF HUMANS!

Use a mini-sticker to choose the right answer.

11

12

14

EGGS AND PUPS

Most fish lay eggs, but some sharks are different—many of them give birth to live young, known as pups, instead.

SHARK FACT

WHALE SHARKS LAY UP TO 300 EGGS AT A TIME AND BLUE SHARKS CAN GIVE BIRTH TO MORE THAN 130 PUPS!

GIVING BIRTH

Sharks that give birth keep their eggs inside them while they grow. A growing pup gets food from its egg, or sometimes from its mother's body.

Lemon shark

Shark pup growing inside an egg.

DON'T EAT MY PUPS!

Horn sharks, dogfish, and swell sharks lay eggs. Each egg is wrapped in a rubbery case called a mermaid's purse. A mother does not take care of her eggs while the pups grow inside them.

LEMON SHARKS

A lemon shark has up to 17 pups growing inside her for about a year before they are born. Newborn pups are already 2 feet (61cm) long.

When the pups are born they swim away from their mother so she doesn't eat them!

The tendrils on an egg case wrap around seaweed and hold the case in place while the pup grows inside.

It can take a year for some eggs to hatch.

TRUE OR FALSE ?

Use your mini-stickers to choose your answers.

1 Some sharks lay eggs.

2 Sharks' eggs are called fairy slippers.

3 Baby sharks are called kittens.

41

SHARKS AND HUMANS

Many people are scared of sharks, but they don't need to be. Sharks have much more reason to be scared of humans!

Sharks are often caught and killed for their fins, which are used to make soup.

SHARK SCIENCE

Scientists study sharks, such as the great white, to find out more about their habits. There is still lots to learn about these amazing fish.

Sharks die when they get caught up in fishing nets.

?

WHICH SHARK?

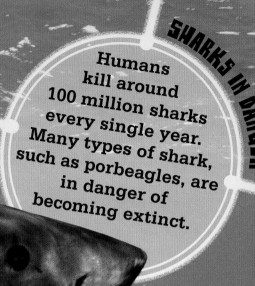

Humans kill around 100 million sharks every single year. Many types of shark, such as porbeagles, are in danger of becoming extinct.

WHO'S MORE SCARY? ME OR YOU?

SHARK ATTACK

Sharks rarely attack people. Fewer than ten people a year are killed by sharks. More people die from bee stings, dog bites, or lightning strikes.

Scientists can get close to sharks using a protective shark cage.

Read the text and choose the correct stickers.

Scientists study this shark.

This shark may become extinct, thanks to humans.

43

SHARK FACTS

LARGEST EVER

The largest whale shark ever was caught in 1949.

17 tons (15.4mton)

41 feet (12.5m)

20 feet (6.1m)

The largest great white shark ever caught was 20 feet (6.1m) long.

Some even bigger sharks lived about 15 million years ago. Megalodon grew to 50 feet (15.2m) and preyed on fish and small whales. They died out about 1.5 million years ago. Or did they?

RECORD BREAKERS

Largest shark...................... Whale shark

Largest hunting shark.... Great white shark

Most common shark........ Spiny dogfish (spurdog)

The biggest hammer.......... Winghead hammerhead

Flattest sharks .... Wobbegongs and angelsharks

Longest tail......................... Thresher shark

Deepest shark...................... Portuguese shark

Warmest body .... Salmon shark

Best vision............................ Great white shark

Best hearing........................ Silky shark

Most dangerous .... Great white shark

Longest-living..................... Spiny dogfish (spurdog)

Best electric sense .... Smooth dogfish

Best leapers.......................... Shortfin mako and manta ray

LARGEST EVER!

Megalodon

FUN ? STUFF

SCRAMBLED EGGS

These sharks all lay eggs. Can you unscramble their names?

1. SLEWL RAKSH ☐☐☐☐☐ ☐☐☐☐☐

2. NORH SHRAK ☐☐☐☐ ☐☐☐☐☐

3. SHIGDOF ☐☐☐☐☐☐☐

SHARK SHAPES

Put a mini-sticker next to the outline of an angelshark.

?

?

?

?

?

?

WHICH SHARK?

This ray gives an electric shock.

This shark can live to 70 years of age.

?

?

?

GLOSSARY

CAMOUFLAGE
Colors, patterns, and shapes on an animal's skin that help it to hide.

CARTILAGE
A bendy substance that sharks have instead of hard bone.

CURRENT
A large movement of water in the ocean.

CUSP
The pointed top, or tops, of a tooth.

ELECTRICITY
A type of energy that powers muscles.

EXTINCT
When a type of animal has died out completely.

GILLS
The organs that sharks and other fish use to breathe underwater.

PECTORAL FINS
Fins on the side of a shark, near its head.

PLANKTON
Tiny animals and plants in the ocean.

PREDATOR
An animal that hunts other animals to eat.

PREY
An animal that is hunted by another one.

PUP
A baby shark.

SENSES
How all animals understand and respond to the world around them, such as by seeing,

hearing, tasting, touching, or smelling things.

SHOAL
A group of fish.

SNOUT
The front of a shark's head, where its nose i

STREAMLINED
A special body shape that allows an animal to move easily throug air or water.

TENDRIL
A stringlike part of a animal or plant that c grow and wrap aroun other things.

VENOM
Poison that is made by an animal and injecte into its victim, usuall via a bite or sting.

ANSWERS

 p3 YES OR NO?
1. Yes
2. No, they live in oceans.
3. Yes

 p6 WHICH SHARK?
Port Jackson shark
Whale shark

 p8 TRUE OR FALSE?
1. False
2. True
3. False

 p11 RAY OR SKATE?
Ray
Skate

p12 TRUE OR FALSE?
1. False, they can have hundreds of teeth.
2. True
3. False

 p14 WHICH SHARK?
Thresher shark
Angelshark

 **p16 SPOT THE DIFFERENCE**
4 differences

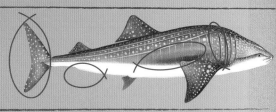

 p19 SCRAMBLED SHARKS
1. H A M M E R H E A D
2. S H O R T F I N   M A K O
3. P O R T   J A C K S O N

 p20 QUICK QUIZ
1. A pig
2. A dwarf lanternshark
3. Sunlight can't reach there.

p22 WHICH SHARK?
Greenland shark

WHICH FISH?

HUNGRY STAN
Stan the stingray eats 10 fish altogether.

p24 WHICH SHARK?
Shortfin mako
Blue shark

 p31 WHICH SHARK?
Basking shark
Ratfish

WORD-WISE
An animal that hunts other animals to eat.

p33 YES OR NO?
1. Yes
2. No, they can see all around.
3. Yes

p35 WHICH SHARK?
Sawshark
Hammerhead

WEIRD BUT TRUE
1. Indian cobras: they kill about 10,000 people in India alone every year.
2. True
3. Basking shark

 p37 WHICH SHARK?
Sandtiger shark
Bull shark

p39 POOR PERCY!
12 sharks are chasing Percy!

p41 TRUE OR FALSE?
1. True
2. False, they are called mermaids' purses.
3. False, they are called pups.

p43 WHICH SHARK?
Great white shark
Porbeagle

SHARK SHAPES

WHICH SHARK?
Spurdog (Spiny dogfish)
Electric ray

 p45 SCRAMBLED EGGS

1. S W E L L   S H A R K   2. H O R N   S H A R K   3. D O G F I S H

ACKNOWLEDGMENTS

This edition published by Scholastic Inc.,
557 Broadway, New York, NY 10012
by arrangement with Quarto publishing.

Scholastic and associated logos are trademarks
and/or registered trademarks of Scholastic Inc.
Distributed by Scholastic Canada Ltd., Markham,
Ontario

Copyright © QEB Publishing, Inc. 2013

Published in the United States by
QEB Publishing, Inc.
3 Wrigley, Suite A
Irvine, CA 92618
www.qed-publishing.co.uk

A CIP record for this book is available from the
Library of Congress.

ISBN: 978-0-545-65514-9

11 10 9 8 7 6 5 4 3 2 1

Printed in Shenzhen City, China

Picture credits
**(t=top, b=bottom, l=left, r=right, c=centre, fc=front
cover, bc=back cover)**
FLPA bc Norbert Wu/Minden Pictures; 4c Mike Parry/Minden
Pictures; 5c Norbert Probst/Imagebroker; 5br Bruno
Guenard/Biosphoto; 6c Colin Marshall; 7tr Norbert Wu/
Minden Pictures; 7b Fred Bavendam/Minden Pictures; 8b
Richard Herrmann/Minden Pictures; 9b Brandon Cole/
Biosphoto; 11bl; Scott Leslie/Minden Pictures; 13tr Kelvin
Aitken/Biosphoto; 14t Gerard Soury/Biosphoto; 16c
OceanPhoto; 17t Norbert Wu/Minden Pictures; 17b Reinhar
Dirscherl; 18c Norbert Probst/Imagebroker; 21t Kelvin
Aitken/Biosphoto; 21c Norbert Wu/Minden Pictures; 19b
Brandon Cole/Biosphoto; 24c Richard Herrmann/Minden
Pictures; 28c /Imagebroker; 29trc Yann Hubert/Biosphoto;
30b Mike Parry/Minden Pictures; 31t Pascal Kobeh/
Biosphoto; 32b Reinhard Dirscherl; 33tc Yann Hubert/
Biosphoto; 34bl Kelvin Aitken/Biosphoto; 35c Bruno
Guenard/Biosphoto; 37c F1online/F1online; 37t Â©
Biosphoto , GÃ©rard Soury/Biosphoto; 38tr Mike Parry/
Minden Pictures; 39trc Mike Parry/Minden Pictures; 40blc
Bruno Cavignaux/Biosphoto; 41bl D P Wilson; Jean-Michel
Mille/Biosphoto; 42blc Fred Bavendam/Minden Pictures;
48b Reinhard Dirscherl; Getty 8tr Franco Banfi; 18bl Gerard
Soury/Getty; Museum Victoria 36bc Dianne Bray/Museum
Victoria; Nature Photo Library 10c Alex Mustard; 20cl Jeff
Rotman; 29b Jurgen Freund/naturepl.com; 40c Doug
Perrine/naturepl.com; 42cr Jeff Rotman; Science Photo
Library 9c Patrice Ceisel, Visuals Unlimited, Inc.; 12bl Andy
Murch/Visuals Unlimited, Inc.; fc, 12c Andy Murch/Visual
Unlimited, Inc.; Shutterstock fc background melissaf84; 11t
mrHanson; 15c A Cotton Photo; 17 background kataleewan
intarachote; 18bl Maximus256; 21t Maximus256; 22bl Lynx
Aqua; 22bl Vilainecrevette; 23br grandboat; 24cr Natykach
Nataliia; 25b Dray van Beeck; 26bl A7880S; 26cr honobono;
26bl, tr, inxti; 27bl Lynx Aqua; 27bl Eric Isselee; 27cl Valerie
Potapova; 27tr Sukharevskyy Dmytro (nevodka); 27 c, tr
inxti; 27br Jim Agronick; 27 background Rich Carey; 29tr
Maximus256; 29 background Vlad61/Shutterstock; 29
background Menna/Shutterstock; 31b Greg Amptman; 31
background Rich Carey; 33t Maximus256; 33 background
Rich Carey; 34 background Rich Carey; 35t Ethan Daniels;
36b Maximus256; 37 background 59248087; 38bl Attila
JANDI; 39tr Maximus256; 40bl Maximus256; 42bl
Maximus256; 44br Catmando